Big Book of Fun

Written by Lesley Young
with illustrations by Ley Honor Roberts
Based on characters created by Jean and Laurent de Brunhoff

Zephir says, 'Take Care!' In this book there are lots of things to do and make. When you are cooking, or using scissors or other craft implements, always ask an adult to help you.

This work conceived, produced and originally published in 1999 by Madcap Books, André Deutsch Ltd., 76 Dean Street, London, W1V 5HA. www.vci.co.uk

Adapted by Lesley Young and Ley Honor Roberts, based on characters created by Jean and Laurent de Brunhoff

Design by Traffika Publishing Limited

A catalogue record for this title is available from the British Library

ISBN 0 233 99542 0

Reprographics by Jade Repographics

Printed in Italy

BIG BOOK OF FUN ANSWERS

HUNT THE CROWNS (page 10-11) - There are seven crowns in the picture.
FLUTTER BY, BUTTERFLY (page 14-15) - There are ten caterpillars and seventeen butterflies.

CONTENTS

COCO CLOWNS

Coco is the clown in Celesteville.
There is never a boring moment when he's around.
Here are some of his tricks.

To fool people, you can cut footprints out of dark-coloured card and place them on a pale carpet.

Pom has cut a large 'spill' of red-coloured paper and put it on Celeste's pale pink carpet, beside a bottle of tomato ketchup.

When she walks in, Celeste has a fright until Pom picks up the 'stain', crumples it and throws it away.

Magic!

AROUND

Coco goes up to Zephir and says, 'Here is some sliced banana and custard for you.'
'My favourite,' says Zephir, taking the bowl of custard, 'but this banana is not even peeled, so how can it be sliced?'
'Peel it and see!' laughs Coco.
Zephir unpeels the banana and it falls,

in neat slices into the bowl of custard.

To do the trick:

Push a cocktail stick through the skin of a banana and move it from side to side. It will cut through the banana while leaving the skin undamaged. Do this a few times, up and down the banana, where you want it to be sliced. Peel the banana and see the pieces fall.

COCO CLOWNS

Coco puts six coins on the ground in an L-shape, with four coins down and three coins across, as shown below. 'Can you move one coin so that both rows have four coins in them?' he asks.

Everyone tries, while Coco watches, laughing and turning somersaults.

'Give up? I'll show you how it's done,' he says, putting coin A on top of coin B.

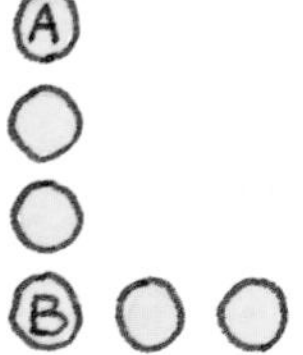

AROUND

Coco takes a copy of the *Jungle Times* and picks out one sheet. 'Paper is made from trees,' he says, 'and I'm going to show you how to turn this paper back into one.' Everyone watches while he rolls and cuts. Soon, he pulls the top of the paper, and, before their very eyes, it grows into a tree.

1. Take a sheet of newspaper and roll it up tightly, starting from one corner.

2. Fasten one end of the roll with a piece of Sellotape.

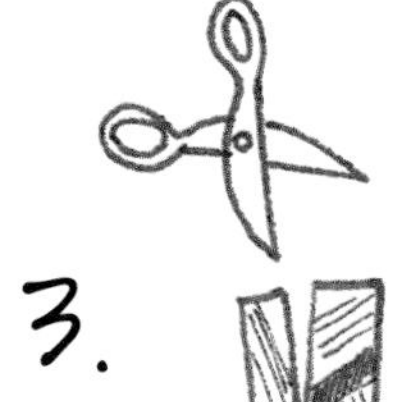

3. At the other end, cut through all the layers to about halfway down the roll. Do this in two or three places.

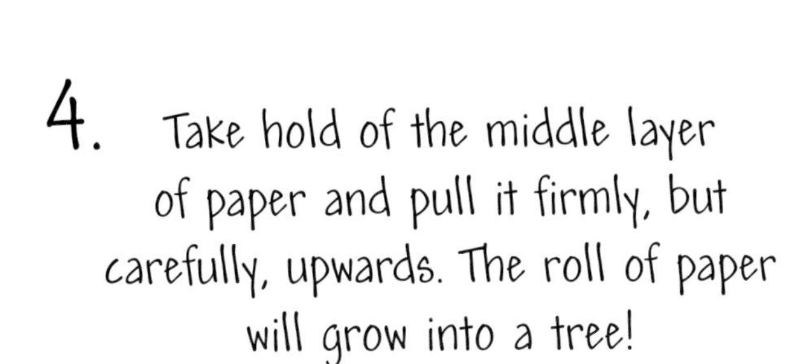

4. Take hold of the middle layer of paper and pull it firmly, but carefully, upwards. The roll of paper will grow into a tree!

COCO CLOWNS

Finally, Babar says to Coco, 'I have a trick for you.'

He produces two paper bags, one with a red crown on it and the other with a blue crown on it. 'Have a look inside and make sure both bags are empty,' says Babar. Everyone – including Coco – has a good look.

Babar now produces two balloons – one red and one blue – and drops the red balloon into the red crown bag and the blue balloon into the blue crown bag.

'Jungle, jangle!' shouts Babar, pulling the red balloon out of the blue crown bag, and the blue balloon from the red crown bag. Everyone gasps and cheers.

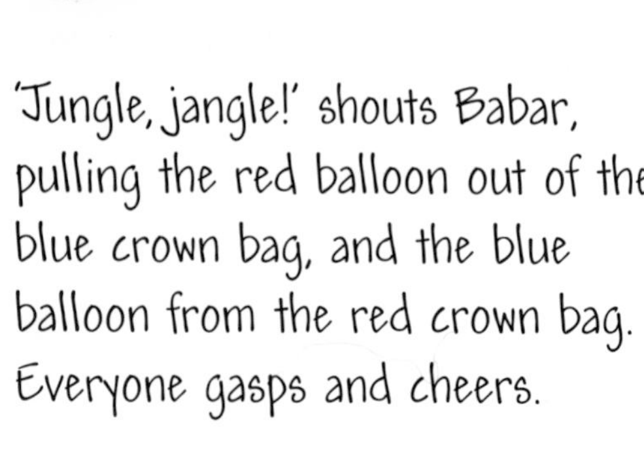

AROUND

You need:
Two paper bags
Red and blue paints
or felt-tip pens
Two red balloons
Two blue balloons
A pencil

How to do it:

You must prepare your bags and balloons on your own, in secret, before you perform this trick.

1. Paint a red crown on one paper bag and a blue crown on the other (or simply draw a crown and fill in with felt-tip pens).

2. Now, push a blue balloon inside a red balloon (it's easy if you use the blunt end of a pencil to help), leaving a little of the neck of the blue balloon sticking out. Push the other red balloon inside the other blue balloon in the same way.

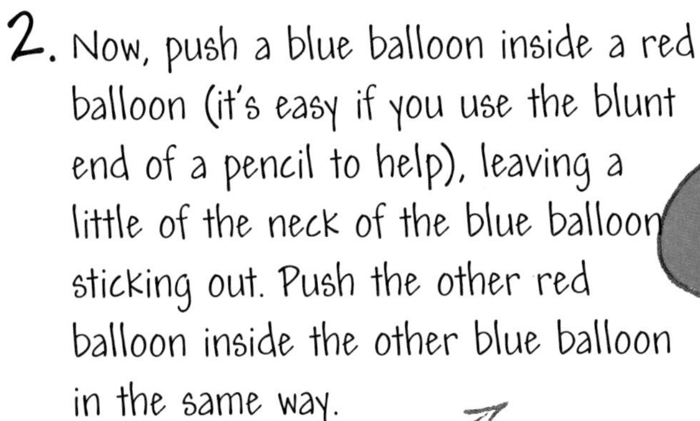

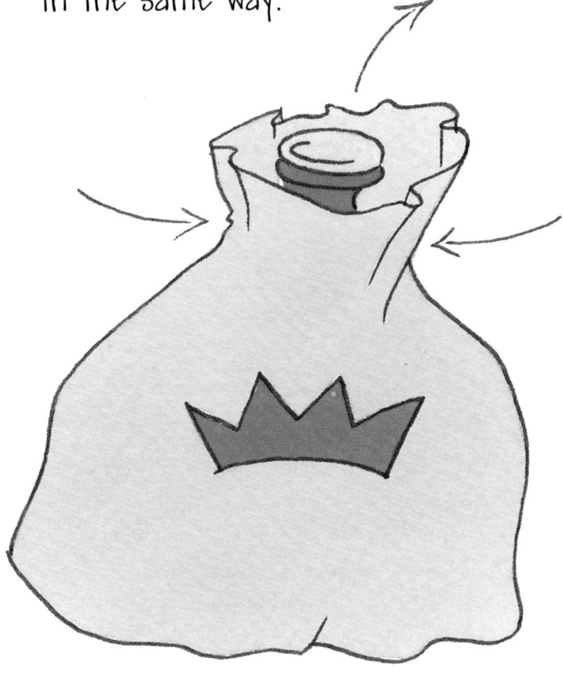

3. When you place each balloon in the bag with the same colour shapes on, cover the neck of the inner balloon with your fingers. After saying your magic words, hold the base of the red balloon firmly - through the paper - and pull the blue balloon inside it out with your other hand, grasping its neck firmly. Crumple the bag, with the red balloon in it, and throw it away. Pull the red balloon out of the bag with the blue crown on it, in the same way. Crumple the bag and throw it away. It will look as if the balloons have magically switched bags! It is a good idea to practice this trick on your own before you perform it.

HUNT THE

How many crowns can you find in the picture?

CROWNS

Flora has been given a set of water paints for her birthday. She finds the perfect spot and settles down to paint a picture of the lake. But suddenly, black clouds appear, there is a crack of lightning, and Flora's picture is drenched in a torrent of rain. Justinen, the painter, appears with an umbrella.

'Don't worry, Flora,' he says. 'These jungle storms never last long. Look – the sun's coming out. Let me show you how easy it is to paint a watercolour.'

You need:

Sheets of specially absorbent paper designed for watercolours (available from art shops)
Watercolour paints
A china watercolour palette with different compartments for mixing paints, or a couple of saucers
A pencil (HB is best)
Brushes – a medium one (like a size 8 sable) and a fine one, to paint detail
Small sponge
Water

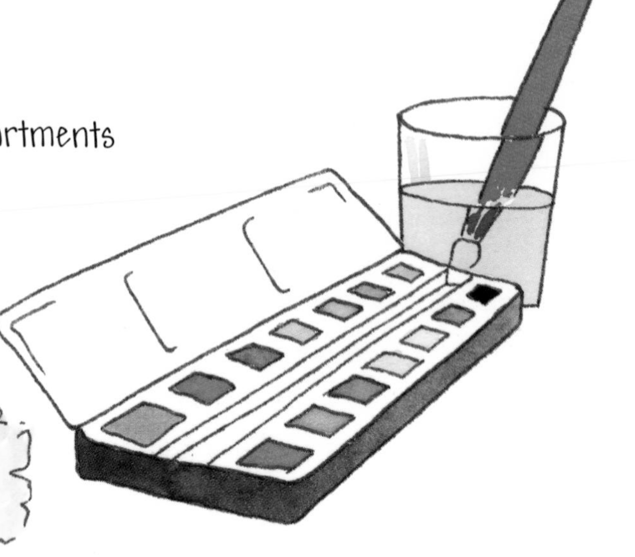

WASHOUT

What to do:

Fix your paper to a board with bulldog clips.

Make a faint pencil drawing of Flora's chosen scene (above). Mix blue paint with water and, starting at the top left-hand corner of the paper, brush the blue across from left to right, to colour the sky. While the paint is wet, press it with a sponge to give the effect of clouds. Mix a darker blue paint and paint the lake in the same way. Leave the picture to dry before adding darker colours, i.e. trees, mountains and the sun.

Painting on wet paper can produce even more exciting pictures.

Flora's colourful swirls, added to a damp sheet of blue paper, all run into each other and spread out, just like fireworks. When it is dry, Flora paints her family watching the fireworks.

FLUTTER BY,

Babar and his family are spending a day in the countryside. Flora is counting caterpillars. 'They're not so easy to count when they turn into butterflies,' says the Old Lady, pointing at Pom and Zephir.

BUTTERFLY
How many caterpillars and butterflies can you find?

BABAR'S FORTUNE

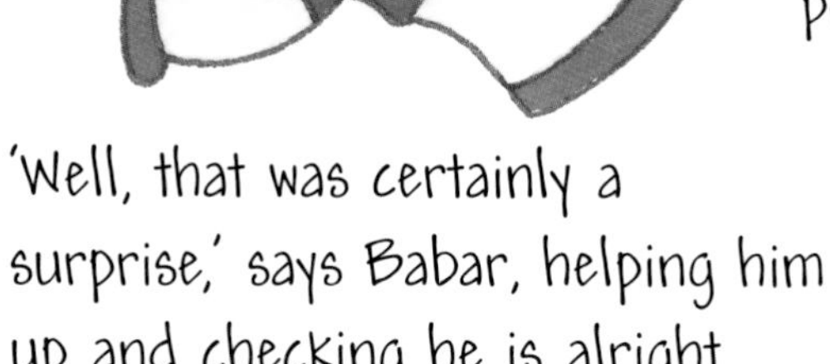

Arthur comes running into the palace waving a small piece of paper. 'Look - it says here that I'm going to have a surprise!' Arthur is so excited that he slips and falls with a bump on the polished palace floor.

'Well, that was certainly a surprise,' says Babar, helping him up and checking he is alright.

'Where did you get that piece of paper?' asks Babar.

'Inside a fortune cookie,' says Arthur.

'Sounds like fun,' says Babar. 'Let's make some for everyone.'

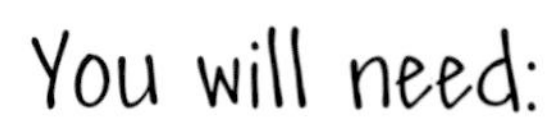

You will need:

A bun tray, greased
Paper baking cases
Greaseproof paper
Plain white paper
A pair of scissors
A pen or pencil
A wire cooling rack

150g (6oz) self-raising flour
a pinch of salt
100g (4oz) soft margarine
100g (4oz) caster sugar
2 large eggs
1 dessertspoon lemon juice
Grated rind of a lemon

For the icing:
A mug of icing sugar, the juice of half a lemon, 2 tablespoons of cocoa.

COOKIES

What to do:

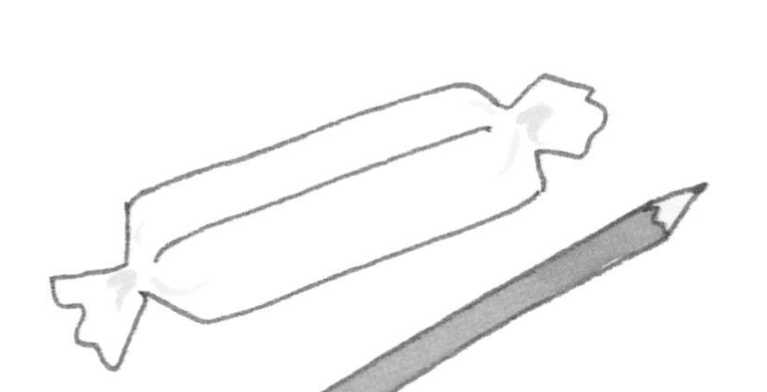

1. First, think up some messages for your cookies. They should, of course, only be happy or funny ones, such as: 'someone will phone with a surprise - Babar says it must be a trunk call!' Write them on squares of greaseproof paper, twisting the ends to seal the parcel.

2. Pre-heat the oven to gas mark 5/375°F/190°C. (Always ask an adult to help you use the oven.)

3. Put all the ingredients into a bowl and beat until completely smooth.

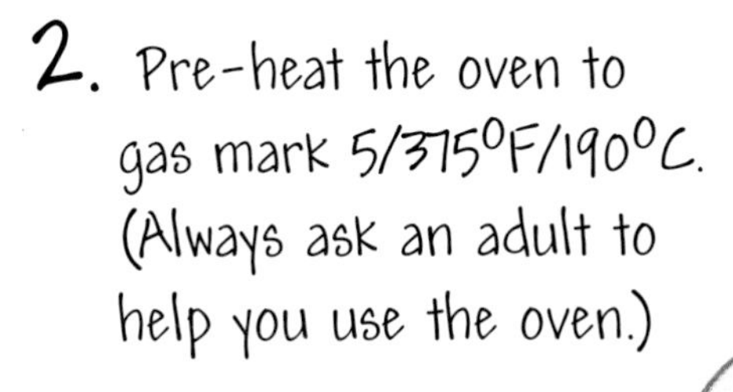

4. Now drop about a teaspoonful of the mixture into each paper case.

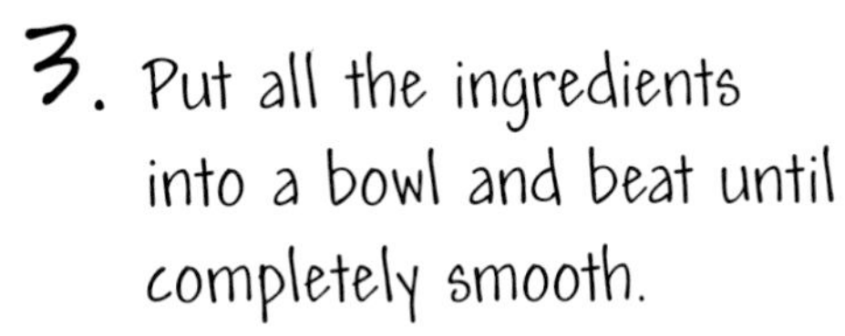

5. Put a message on top of the mixture in each case and cover with another teaspoonful of mixture.

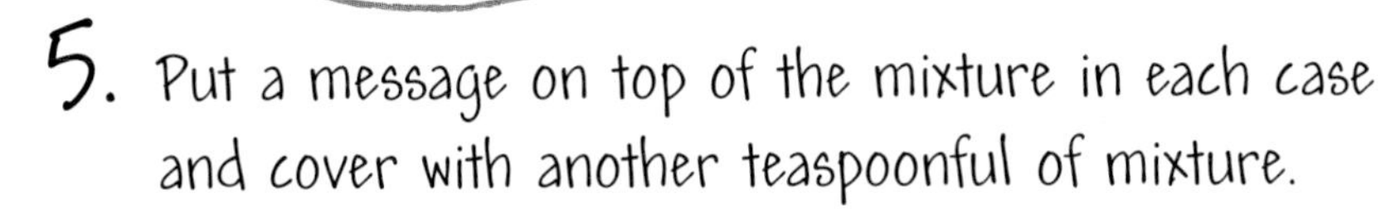

6. Bake on a shelf just above the centre of the oven for 15-20 minutes, or until the cakes are well-risen and golden-brown in colour.

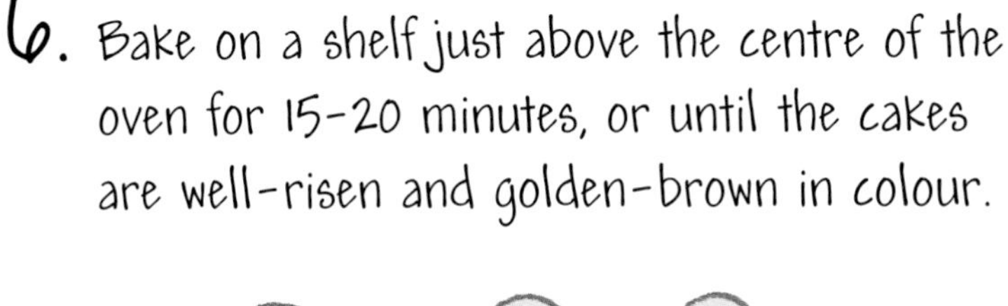

7. Using oven gloves, remove the bun tray from the oven, place on a heat-resistant surface and leave to cool.

8. Half fill a mug with icing sugar. Add the juice from half a lemon, until you have icing that is smooth and not too runny. When the cakes are cool, ice them with the lemon icing.

JUNGLE

To make this jungle snake puppet, you need:

A long sock
Brightly-coloured felt (including red)
A pair of scissors
Fabric glue
Needle and thread
Two buttons

What to do:

1. Pull the sock over your hand and push the material down between your thumb and fingers to make a mouth.

SNAKE

2. Sew, or glue on, two buttons for eyes.

3. Cut a long zigzag shape out of felt and glue along the top of the snake.

4. Cut a long, forked tongue out of red felt and glue in place in the mouth.

Zephir has made a lizard by adding a zigzag crest down the back of the snake.

You can also make snake puppets out of the cut-off legs of old pairs of tights. Glue on a long fabric tongue, and add bits of brightly-coloured silk, glitter or sequins.

PAPER

Arthur is going for a walk.
He wants to do some drawing.

'Can we come, Arthur?' shout Flora, Pom and Alexander.
'Alright,' says Arthur, 'but I've only got one pencil. Perhaps we could share the paper.'
'But what can we make with paper if we have no pencils or paints?' asks Pom.

PLAY

Some time later, an aeroplane flies overhead. 'Oh, look at that!' says a very excited Alexander, 'I'd love to fly a plane.'

'Perhaps you can,' says Arthur as he pulls a piece of paper out of his sketch book. The three children look on in amazement as Arthur folds the paper. Soon, he has made a paper aeroplane and written ALEXANDER on the wing.

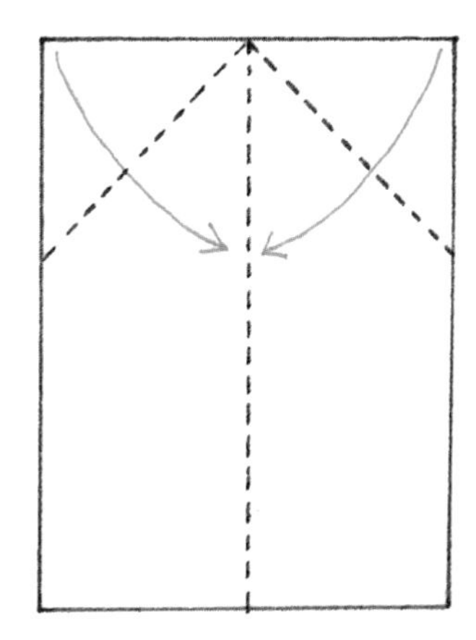

Make a crease down the middle of the paper, then fold in the corners to the middle crease.

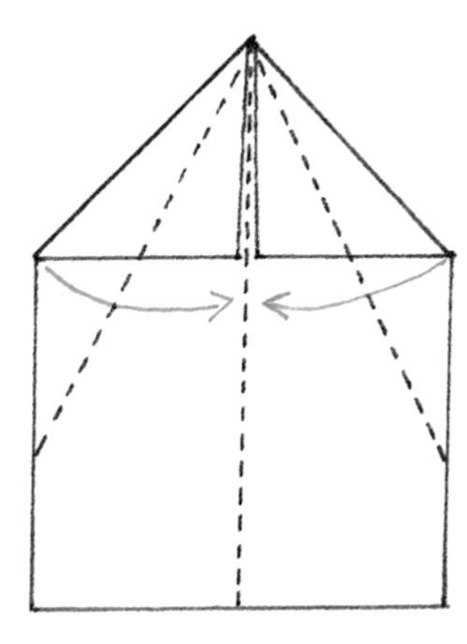

Fold the sides in again to the middle crease.

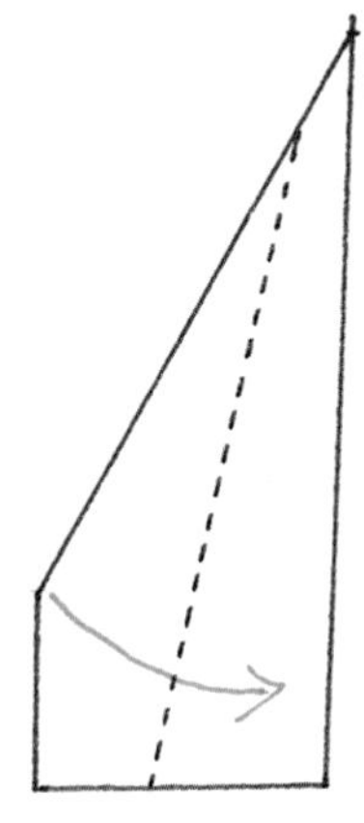

Fold in half and then fold back the wings.

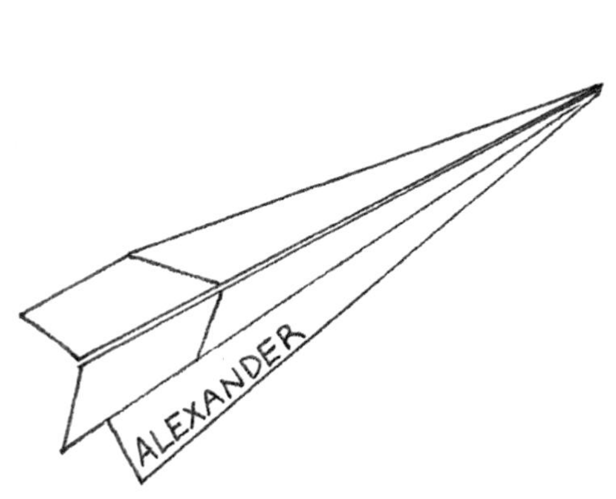

Throw into the air and watch it fly.

PAPER
The plane flies past a sycamore tree and knocks off a seed. The seed twirls to the ground.
'It's a helicopter,' shouts Flora. 'Can we make one of those as well?' Arthur gets another piece of paper and starts tearing and folding.
Tear along the two red lines.
Fold in the flaps.
Fold the bottom of the flap up.
Tear down the red line.
Fold down the top flaps, one backwards, one forwards.
Throw the helicopter into the air and watch it spin to the ground.

PLAY

Pom has spotted some blackberries. 'My favourite,' he says.

'We'll make a bag to put them in,' says Arthur.

Pom is now busy picking blackberries. Flora is playing with her helicopter and Alexander is throwing his plane into the air. And Arthur – he's drawing, of course!

MAKING

Zephir has been invited to a Fancy Dress Party at the palace. Everyone is going to make a mask, and Zephir has decided to make a Babar mask.

You will need:

A pencil
A white paper plate
Thin white card
Corrugated cardboard
A pair of scissors
Glue
A hole punch
Elastic
Paints and brush

What to do:

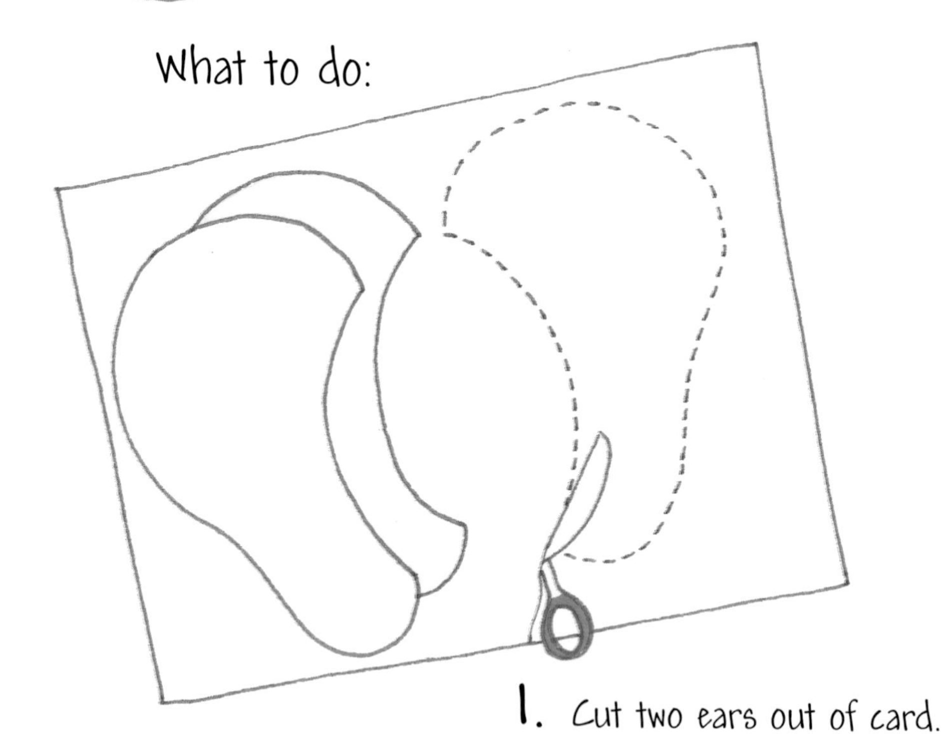

1. Cut two ears out of card.
2. Cut a trunk out of the corrugated card, with the lines running from left to right.
3. Cut out two tusks.

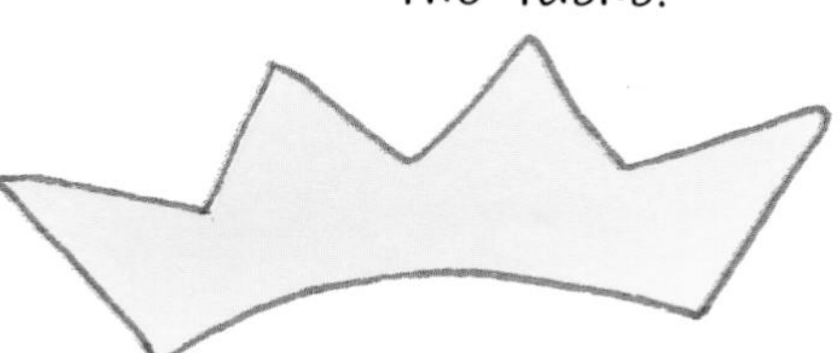

4. Cut out a crown and paint it yellow.

MASKS

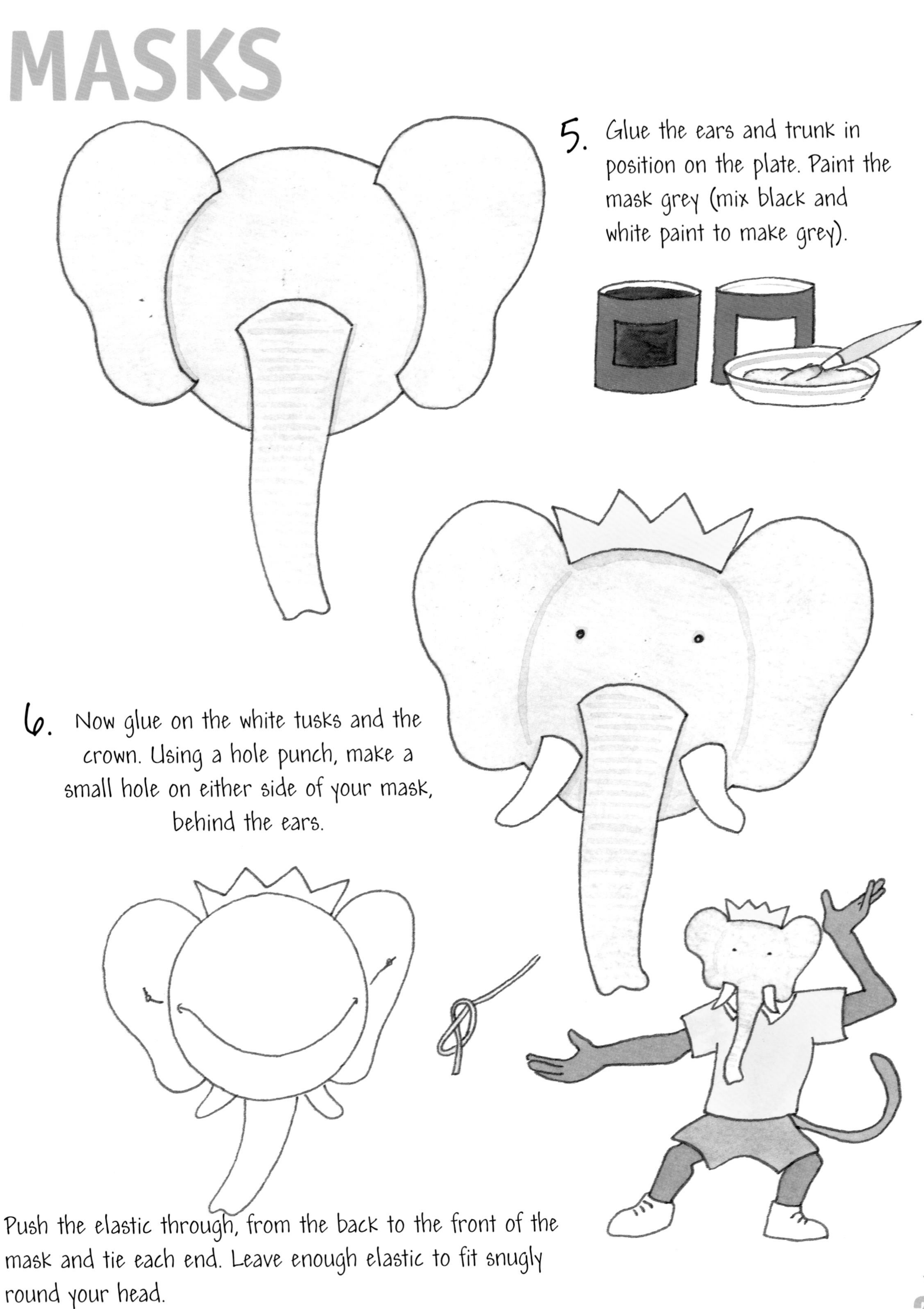

5. Glue the ears and trunk in position on the plate. Paint the mask grey (mix black and white paint to make grey).

6. Now glue on the white tusks and the crown. Using a hole punch, make a small hole on either side of your mask, behind the ears.

Push the elastic through, from the back to the front of the mask and tie each end. Leave enough elastic to fit snugly round your head.

MAKING
Jungle Beetle
Copy and cut out this body shape and six legs from thin card. Glue the legs in place. Paint the beetle in bright colours before gluing on two eyes. Thread beads onto pipecleaners and fix at the top of the head. Finally, cut out eye holes and add elastic.

MASKS

Clown

Cut eye holes into a paper plate and paint round each. Add a wide red mouth and black triangles for eyebrows. Cut out a bow tie and hat from card, paint them and then glue on to the face. Glue on the lid from a tube of Smarties for the nose, and glue on gold pan scrubbers for the hair. Why not add a few streamers to the clown's hat, to finish it off?

FLORA'S

Flora is playing in the garden and is covered in mud.
'Time for your bath,' calls Celeste.
'I'm having fun - I don't want a bath,' says Flora.
'Wait till you see this bath!' says Celeste.

FIZZY BATH

To make fizzy bath salts, mix together a level tablespoon of sodium bicarbonate and a level teaspoon of citric acid (you can buy these from a chemist).
Add a few drops of essential oil if you like - pine or lavender are good. If you add lemon oil, you will feel as if you are bathing in lemonade!
Sprinkle the mixture into a full bath.

When Flora sees how her bath water is fizzing and popping, she jumps in and doesn't want to get out.

BEACH

The beach is a great place for a party, with lots of room to run around and play games.

CRAB RACE

Mark out two lines on the sand. The players have to crawl on hands and knees from one to the other. To make it harder, they must travel sideways, just like crabs.

MAD HATTER

Make your own paper hat and decorate it with things found on the beach.

PARTY

SEAGULLS

Babar says, 'Have fun - and don't forget to take your litter home with you.'

Sit together, and blow as hard as you can to keep a feather in the air. If it lands on you, you lose.

COINS IN THE BUCKET

Fill a bucket with water. Drop a couple of one pence pieces in. Each player is given four shells, and they take turns to drop one in the bucket and try to cover the smaller coins.

BEACH

OBSTACLE RACE

Choose a stretch of beach for your track, then mark out a piece of sand to jump over. Get two people to hold a beach towel stretched out about a metre above the sand for players to crawl under. Leave a skipping rope on the sand for players to skip through ten times. Finally, build a sandcastle to jump over.

PARTY

SAND SCULPTURE

Get everyone to build something out of sand, and give a prize for the best sculpture.

CUT IT

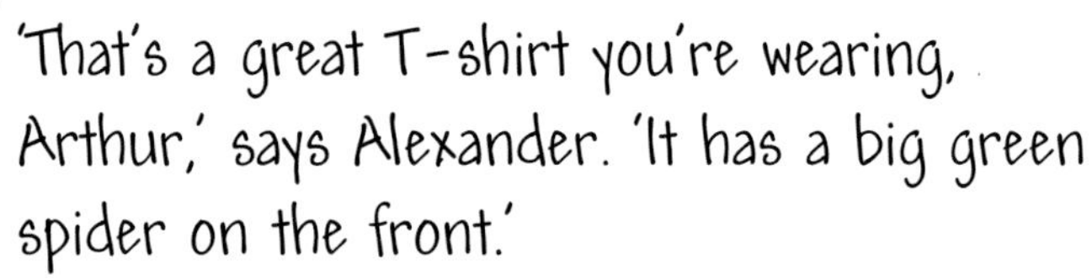

'That's a great T-shirt you're wearing, Arthur,' says Alexander. 'It has a big green spider on the front.'

'I made the picture myself,' says Arthur. 'I cut a stencil out of a banana leaf. It's really easy. Let me show you how.'

You need:

Thin card and paper
Tracing paper
A felt-tip pen
Masking tape
A craft knife (ask a grown-up to help you with this)
Newspapers
Poster or acrylic paint
A paint brush (or a small sponge)
A saucer

What to do:

Draw the design you want to stencil on to a piece of paper. You might choose to copy the spider shown here.

Trace the design onto tracing paper. Fix the tracing paper firmly on to the thin card with masking tape. Cut out the design, cutting through the tracing paper and the card. Now place a board on the table so you don't accidentally scratch the table. Craft knives are very sharp, so ask a grown-up to help with this bit. Cut out the smallest spaces first, and leave good joining bits (bridges) between the spaces.

OUT

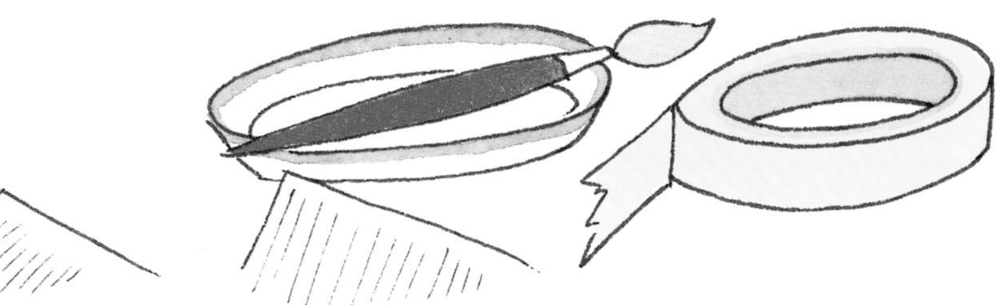

Cover a table with newspaper. Tape the stencil to plain paper or card with masking tape. Dip your brush (or sponge) into a saucer of paint, and dab it to get rid of any excess.

Your brush or sponge should not have too much paint on it because paint can then seep under your stencil. Hold the brush upright and dab all over the stencil until the spaces are filled in. Gently lift off the stencil to see your pattern. Wipe the stencil clean if you want to re-use it.

CUT IT

You can stencil greetings cards, sheets of paper to cover books, posters, etc. You could also stencil a plain white T-shirt, like Arthur's. (Wash it first). Put a piece of cardboard inside the T-shirt to stop your picture going through to the back.

Stencil in the same way as above, but use special fabric paints which are easy to find in art and craft shops.

OUT

Arthur has decorated his bedroom, stencilling stars and moons across his walls with paint that glows in the dark.

'What kind of cake should I make for Babar's birthday?' asks Celeste.
'Banana!' cries Zephir, swinging in through the window.
'Chocolate,' says Pom. 'Is there any other kind?'

PANCAKE

'They both sound very sweet,' says the Old Lady, who has stopped by with a present for Babar. 'You know, there's some lovely spinach in the palace gardens.'
'All right, all right,' says Celeste. 'I have an idea for something that will please all of you.'

Basic Pancake Mix

(100g) 4oz plain flour
a pinch of salt
1 large egg
(200ml) 7 fl oz milk, mixed with (75ml) 3fl oz water
2 tablespoons melted butter

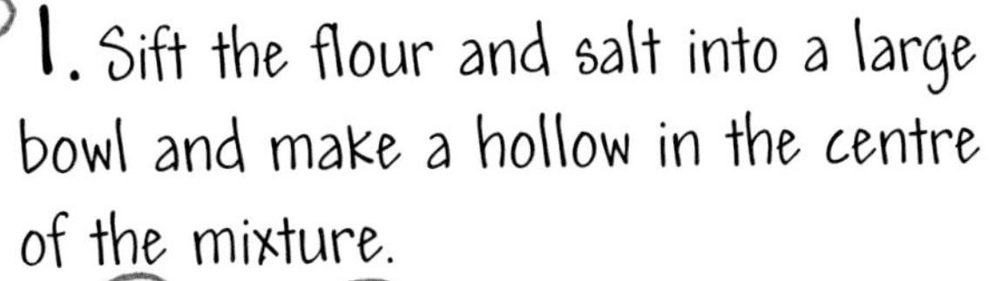

1. Sift the flour and salt into a large bowl and make a hollow in the centre of the mixture.

2. Break the egg into the hollow and mix in the flour from round the edges.

3. Add the milk and water slowly, until you have a thin, creamy batter.

4. Beat the mixture well with your wooden spoon. Just before cooking the pancakes, stir in the melted butter.

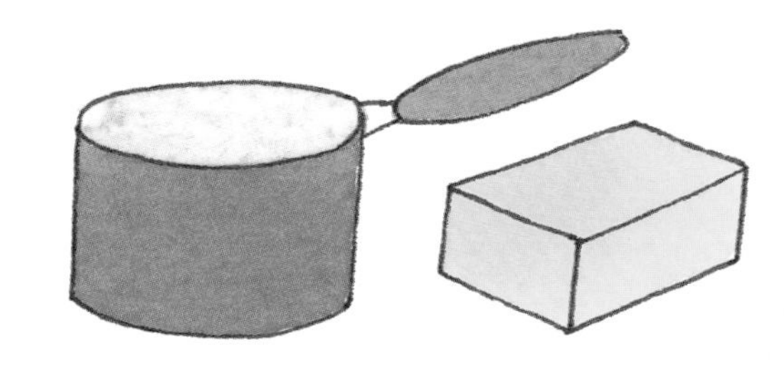

Celeste says: Ask a grown-up to help with the next stage.

5. Grease a heavy frying pan with a little butter. When it is hot, pour in about two tablespoons of batter and tilt the pan so the mixture covers the base evenly. When the pancake is cooked underneath (with bubbles breaking on the surface), carefully turn it over and cook the other side, or toss it if you are brave enough. Slide the cooked pancake on to a plate and keep warm while you make the rest. This mixture should make about 9–12 pancakes.

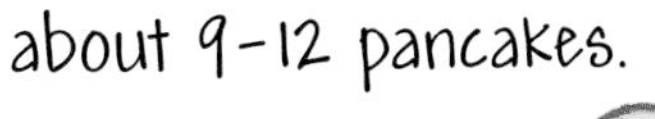

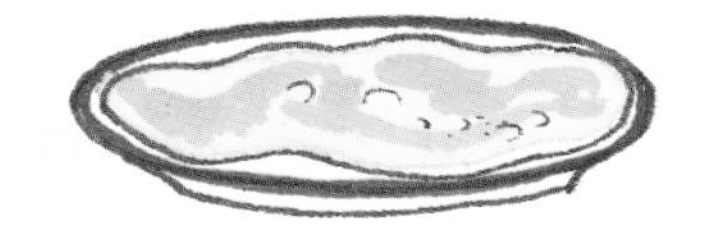

PANCAKE

Banana and Honey Pancakes

Chop two bananas, pour over a tablespoon of lemon juice and mix well. Gently heat four tablespoons of honey in a small pan until just melted. Add half the honey to the bananas, place a generous dollop of filling in each pancake and roll up. Pour the rest of the honey over the rolled-up pancakes and serve. These are delicious with vanilla icecream.

Chocolate Pancakes

Instead of 100g(4oz) plain flour, use 75g(3oz) plain flour and 25g(1oz) sweetened drinking chocolate in the basic pancake mixture. Follow directions as before and serve with whipped cream and crumbled chocolate flake.

Spinach and Cheese Pancakes

Cook (500g) 1lb of fresh spinach - or a small packet of frozen spinach - drain well and stir over a gentle heat to make sure it is not too wet. Chop up 50g(2oz) mature Cheddar cheese and add to the spinach. Fill a couple of pancakes with the mixture. Place in a well-buttered, ovenproof dish and cover generously with grated cheese. Put in a pre-heated oven (gas mark 6/400°F/200°C) for about ten minutes, until the cheese is golden and bubbling.

PALACE

Leaning Tower of Pancakes

Prepare different sweet fillings, such as mashed bananas, chocolate, syrup, marshmallows, sweets and jam. Place a pancake on a plate and spread one kind of filling on top. Put another pancake on top, add another filling and build up your tower by sandwiching together different fillings in this way. If the tower is really high, it will begin to lean. Be careful!

Pour over a sauce (e.g. melted chocolate or cream) and decorate with marshmallows, chocolate flakes, smarties, etc.

ALL WRAPPED

It is fun to design your own wrapping paper, and it makes gifts really special. One of the best and easiest ways to do this is with potato prints.

You need:

Two potatoes
Poster or acrylic paint
A paintbrush
A craft, or sharp vegetable knife
A saucer
Newspapers
Plain paper
A pencil

What to do:

First, draw the design you want to print on some scrap paper. Simple shapes work best - a duck, a flower, a Christmas tree.

Cut a potato in half. Mark the shape you have designed on the cut half.

Now, with the craft knife, cut the potato away from the shape, as shown. Ask a grown-up to help with this bit.

UP

Place the plain paper on to a pile of newspapers.
Mix some paint in the saucer. Brush the potato print with paint.

Space the prints evenly on the paper, as shown. Plain brown wrapping paper looks wonderful if you print it with gold paint. You could make prints of the initials of whoever the present is for.

Make gift tags from luggage labels and thread through ribbon.

FLY A

There are many kinds of kite. Here, you can learn how to make a Japanese kite. It is in the shape of a fish – like the huge, brightly-coloured fish which swim in the lake at Celesteville.

You need:

Tissue paper
A pair of scissors
A pencil and paper
A strong smooth stick (approx. 12 inches long)
A strip of cardboard measuring 2cm x 20cm
Strong thread
A needle
Glue
A stapler

What to do:

1. Draw a fish shape on two sheets of tissue paper (one on top of the other) and cut out.

2. Cut scales from tissue paper and glue onto the body.

Cut eyes from circles of tissue paper and glue in place.

Cut fins from tissue paper.

KITE

3. Slip fins between the two fish shapes and glue the fish shapes together round the edge - leaving the mouth end open.

4. Overlap the ends of the cardboard strip and staple them to make a circle. Put the circle inside the fish's mouth, fold the edge of the tissue back over the cardboard and glue in place.

5. Thread a needle with 25cm of strong thread. Push it through one side of the mouth, tie it round the cardboard strip, and push it through the opposite side of the mouth.

6. Leave enough thread to make a loop across the fish's mouth, then tie the end of the thread round the cardboard loop. Fasten a long length of thread to the stick and tie the other end to the centre of the loop across the fish's mouth. When the wind blows, fly your fish across the sky.

DANCING

Make a row of dancing elephants!

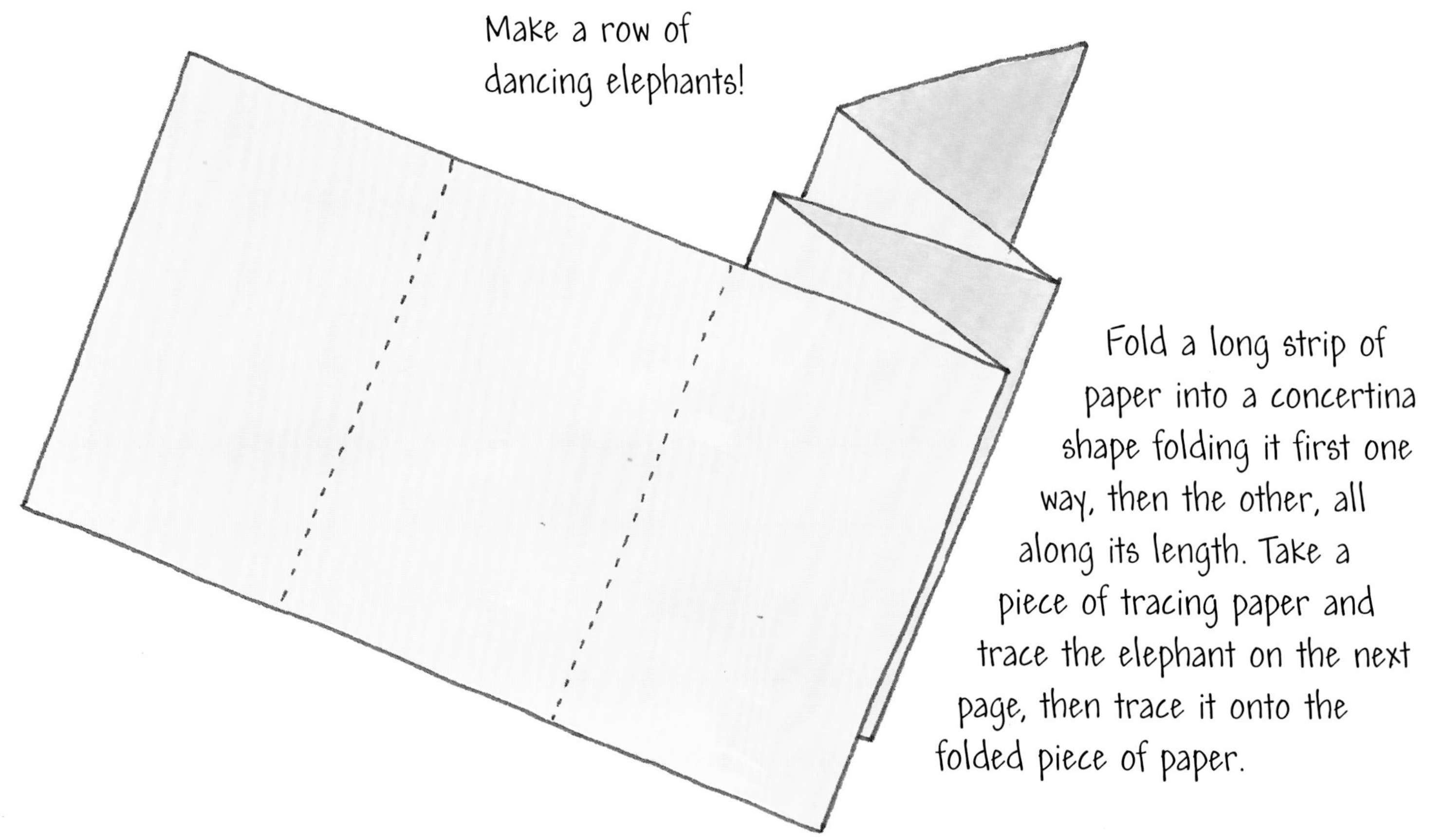

Fold a long strip of paper into a concertina shape folding it first one way, then the other, all along its length. Take a piece of tracing paper and trace the elephant on the next page, then trace it onto the folded piece of paper.

ELEPHANTS

Now, cut along the dotted line, leaving the left-hand fold uncut. Open up your paper and you will have a line of dancing elephants. Use the elephants to decorate gifts, or glue them round the top of your bedroom wallpaper as a border frieze.

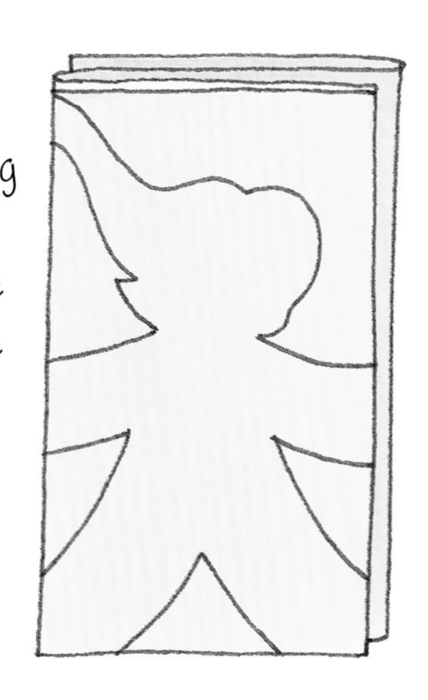

Make lots of elephants or trees like these ones, out of silver or gold paper and hang them up as Christmas decorations.

Goodbye!